COVID-19 BUNDLE

Corona, The Great
Reset & Unreported
Truths about COVID
and Lockdowns

Sigeel A. Marcs

Introduction

More than 2,900 patients have already died from the new coronavirus that first appeared in the Chinese metropolis of Wuhan; 85,000 people have been infected. That number continues to rise rapidly, largely because the virus is transmissible person to person. The virus also has spread outside China, to America, Australia, Europe, and the Middle East. Panic should be avoided, yet vigilance is required. In this book, we list the current facts. What do we know about the so-called 2019-nCoV virus? How did it originate? What can we do about it? How can the spread be contained?

What is it?

The 2019-nCoV virus is a hitherto unknown variant of the coronavirus. Two other known variants are SARS (severe acute respiratory syndrome) and MERS (Middle East respiratory syndrome), that were prevalent at the end of 2002 and in 2014, respectively. Coronaviruses can cause common colds in adults, but an infection can also be deadly.

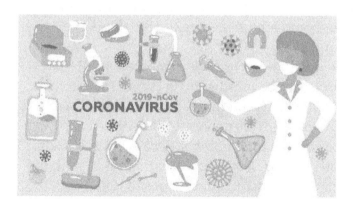

What are the symptoms?

The symptoms resemble those of the flu, with fever and coughing, just like with SARS. At later stages, respiratory problems can occur and the virus can move to the lungs. "The virus will infect the vast majority of people's upper respiratory tract," explains Professor Steven Callens, a virologist at the UZ Gent, Belgium. "A cold, a bronchitis. In diabetics, people with kidney or lung problems... it could become a more serious pneumonia. If people have a hard cough and a high fever, a doctor should be contacted."

The incubation period is estimated at 2-14 days. People can be infected even before symptoms occur (such as coughing, muscle, headaches, and acute fever). This makes it more difficult to estimate the total number of cases. Worldwide more than 85,000 people are diagnosed with the virus, a number that continues to rise.

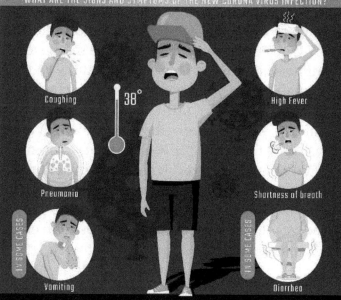

Where did it come from?

The 2019-nCoV virus probably originated at an animal market in Wuhan, a city in the Chinese province of Hubei with 11 million inhabitants. This market was subsequently closed. The exact source has not yet been identified but the new coronavirus likely jumped from an animal to humans. Usually, mammals are the vectors for similar viruses: for MERS I was camels and for SARS the Civet cat. Some speculate that several animal-to-human events occurred at the Wuhan animal market. An animal doesn't have to be eaten to spread the virus.

Initially, it was thought that the 2019-nCoV virus was only transmissible from animals to humans, but it now appears it can be transmitted human to human. One likely transmission is through droplets in the air when someone coughs or sneezes. The fact that people can pass it to each other speeds up the spread precipitously.

Table of contents

Disclaimer

Although the author and publisher have made every effort to ensure that the information in this book was correct at press time, the author and publisher do not assume and hereby disclaim any liability to any party for any loss, damage, or disruption caused by errors or omissions, whether such errors or omissions result from negligence, accident, or any other cause.

This book is not intended as a substitute for the medical advice of physicians. The reader should regularly consult a physician in matters relating to his/her health and particularly concerning any symptoms that may require diagnosis or medical attention.

How deadly is the coronavirus?

We do not yet know whether the new coronavirus (COVID-19) is more serious than the common flu. The official figures now do not seem especially disturbing yet. But we cannot quantify time lags in data reporting, nor intended under-reporting by countries.

The critical point is that it is a new virus, and we do not *know* the potential implications. It is thus important to obtain as much detailed information as possible to determine exactly how dangerous the virus is. More information is needed about the spread of the virus, even among people who become only slightly ill or not sick at all. When people get sick, we need to know exactly where they have been and what they have done.

The 2019-nCoV virus can be lethal, but in the majority of cases, it is not. If the lungs no longer supply the body with enough oxygen due to the condition, other organ functions may fail. Complications may occur in patients who are already suffering from certain diseases, such as diabetes. The fatalities so far have mainly been elderly people and patients who already had an illness. As such, lethality is often indirect and associated with the elderly or others that are not in good health.

More than 85,000 patients are known to be infected with the virus— already higher than that of the SARS epidemic in 2002-2003. SARS killed about 800 people in 2003, a mortality rate between 5 and 15 percent. Approximately 2,900 people have died from the 2019-nCoV virus in recent months.

For comparison, last year 140,000 people worldwide died from measles (for which we have a vaccine), 770,000 from HIV, 405,000 from malaria, and 1,500,000 from tuberculosis. Tens, even hundreds, of thousands of people are killed each year by the common flu.

Because it is unknown how many people have the virus but are not diagnosed, it is not possible to express with precision how deadly the virus is. CNN reported a 2.3% mortality, which would mean the new virus is less lethal than SARS and certainly than MERS (the latter had a mortality rate was 35%). However, a relatively high proportion of cases are considered to be "serious," and only a few patients who have been cured have been discharged from the hospital.

Specific treatments for coronaviruses do not yet exist. Doctors can only combat the symptoms, such as ensuring that patients can breathe freely.

In principle, the immune system of healthy people should be able to cope with the virus. The virus may spread around the world, but in time the hope is that people become more resistant or a vaccine is developed.

How does the virus spread?

The virus spreads between people through invisible little droplets (that we cough and breathe), within two meters. Further than this distance, the virus does not spread.

Generally speaking, the sicker the patient, the more contagious.

In these 'droplets', the virus also spreads through smooth surfaces, such as door handles and surfaces. For example, if people inadvertently leave droplets when they cough or sneeze in their hand and then touch a surface.

This is why it is so important to wash hands and sneeze in the elbow. By the way, it is not possible to say exactly how long the virus survives on a surface, as this depends on the circumstances.

Researchers from the University of Hong Kong figured out how long the SARS virus can survive on a slippery surface. The SARS virus is a virus remarkably similar to the new coronavirus. The virus was found to survive at 22 to 25 degrees and a humidity of 40 to 50 percent, up to five days.

However, the amount of virus decreases rapidly. After 24 hours there is already ten times less virus on keyboards, for example. The same goes for everything with a more or less smooth handle.

So, there are no indications that the coronavirus spreads through the air, like the much more contagious measles disease. But that does include a stroke of the arm. The fact that the virus has not been detected in 'floating' droplets does not mean that it never occurs. For example, the related measles virus was found in hospital air.

Recent research has shown that the SARS virus could theoretically, also be floating.

How can you protect yourself?

Dr. Maria Van Kerkhove of the WHO recommends taking the same precautions as for the flu, e.g., good hygiene, such as washing hands more than usual, and certainly after work or when using public transport. Preferably have no contact with people who are infected or suspected of being infected.

If you have to travel to China, it is imperative to avoid markets with live animals and street stalls where you do not know how the food is prepared.

If you have serious flu symptoms, it is best to contact your general practitioner, especially if you think there could be a link with an affected region in China. Unless a person is sick, going to the emergency room is not immediately necessary (with perhaps the exception of the weak and elderly).

How to prevent proliferation?

David Heymann of the WHO does says that doctors must identify who an infected patient has come in contact with to prevent further spread. Those recent contacts are placed under "fever surveillance." If they have a fever, they will be tested for the virus immediately. If the result is positive, contacts of the new patient are traced. Doctors also must take the necessary precautions not to become infected themselves.

A mask?

We otherwise see people with mouth masks on streets of China (often for reasons associated with pollution), and that is a commonplace sight now.

Only professional, surgical mouth masks offer enough protection. With simpler masks, effects are limited. Viruses are too small and can pass through them. Respecting hygiene measures is, therefore, is more important than wearing a simple mask.

In Wuhan, it is currently mandatory for those who go into public. At least 30 factories produce 8 million or more pieces a day. Yet it is increasingly difficult to get a mouth mask.

What can I do to prevent spreading?

The most important measures you can take to prevent the spread of the coronavirus are very simple. The same measures apply to viruses that cause flu and colds.

- Cough and sneeze on the inside of your elbow.
- Use paper handkerchiefs and throw them away.
- Wash your hands regularly and use an alcohol-based disinfectant whenever possible, especially after interacting with other people.
- If you wash your hands, wash with soap for 20 seconds.
- Wash your hands immediately after sneezing or coughing.
- Avoid crowded places when possible.

- Avoid touching your eyes, nose, or mouth with your hands. Avoid touching your face in general.
- Avoid contact with someone who is ill.
- Clean areas of your home/office using disinfectant wipes.
- If you are in a busy environment (or if someone in your home or office is sick), wear a surgical face mask and encourage those who are sick to wear face masks.

Do you have to worry if you're pregnant?

No.
There is no known increased risk of miscarriage
or birth defects due to infection with this virus.

Can the virus be spread through money?

In China, numerous measures are being enacted to prevent spread of the virus and, apparently, "disinfecting" money is one of them. Yet the chance of people getting infected through money is small.

As far as parcels from China are concerned, these typically are in transit for days. If there was a coronavirus associated with a package, the virus likely would not survive transit time.

Further advice

Groups:
At home, you will receive a maximum of three people per day.
For indoor areas, a maximum number of 30 persons is recommended.
Keep groups smaller than 4 persons for a 1 household.
For outside, a maximum of 4 persons or 1 household.

Daily life:
Work at home unless it is impossible.
Wear a mask in the public indoor spaces and on public transport.

Traveling:
Travel as little as possible.
Stay at your vacation address as much as possible.
Limit the number of trips and avoid crowds.

"It is up to all of us. Do not be the stubborn person who looks for the edges. Be the person who takes responsibility when it comes down to it and that is now!
The measures have an effect on our behavior, and our behavior has an effect on the number of infections. Let us care for each other.

Are we working on a vaccine?

It is not yet clear when a vaccine will be on the market. Scientists around the world are working on a vaccine, but even if they develop one, the virus is already widespread. Moreover, a vaccine is only useful for those who have not yet contracted the Wuhan virus.

Candidate vaccines are made first. After they have been tested for safety and efficacy on animals, testing on humans is typically conducted in three phases. All the phases of development may take 1-2 years depending on particular circumstances.

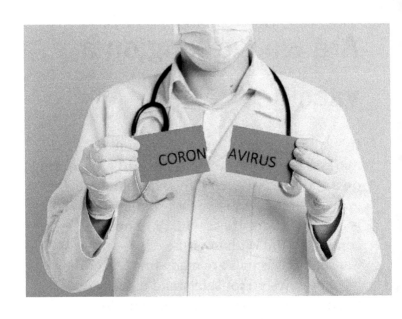

Travel

All non-essential travel to China is currently discouraged by several countries. Tour operators in many countries have canceled all trips to China.

For the time being, Chinese travel agencies are no longer allowed by the government to sell domestic or foreign travel packages. The authorities have closed part of the Great Wall of China, as well as other tourist attractions such as the Forbidden City in Beijing and Disneyland in Shanghai.

Hong Kong introduced an entry ban on residents of Hubei Province and those who have visited Hubei in the last 14 days. The city has also closed many border crossings with China. Russia closed the border with China.

Many countries have repatriated their nationals from Wuhan, where the new coronavirus broke out at the beginning of December. Australia located the evacuated civilians in quarantine on Christmas Island, some 2,000 km from the Australian mainland.

Several airlines have canceled all flights to and from China.

China itself has quarantined several metropolises, including Wuhan. Public transport is sparse in many places and airports and train stations are closed to departing passengers. All inhabitants of the city of Wuhan were asked not to leave the metropolis. Twenty other cities have enacted similar measures. These precautionary measures should slow down the international spread.

Preventive testing on return from a risk area?

No, because that does not provide certainty. If you are infected with the virus, there is not enough virus in the body to be detected for the first few days. A test would not yet show that you are infected with COVID-19. It is common to only be tested for the presence of the virus when people have symptoms and/or come from a known risk area or situation.

Is going on a cruise ship a sensible idea right now?

No.
An infectious disease can break out in an
environment where many people are close for
long periods.

Healing from the coronavirus

How quickly can you heal after infection?

This depends on the severity of the symptoms. People with mild symptoms heal quite quickly, often within a few days. People who have been admitted to the hospital generally need more time to recover (perhaps weeks). The number of people who have recovered lags behind the number of new patients.

Additional information

Can the virus be spread by air?

By coughing and sneezing the virus is expelled from the nose, throat, or lungs. The virus is in the air in small droplets. These droplets do not float and descend quickly. The sicker a person is, the more virus they can spread. There is no evidence that the virus can remain in the air for prolonged periods.

How long does the virus survive outside the body?

A virus always needs a human or animal host to survive and be transmitted. Outside the body, the virus can only survive for a short time. It is still unknown exactly how long that is.

Does the virus spread through food?

This coronavirus has most likely spread from animals to humans. Many animals are brought together in markets and these conditions make it easier for viruses to be transferred from one animal to another, and also from an animal to humans. As a result of human-to-human infections, the virus spreads further. None of these transmission pathways include food.

Is the virus transmissible via mosquitoes?

No, the virus is certainly not transmissible via mosquitoes. It is spread human to human through droplets when coughing and sneezing. Whether animals still play a role in transmission is under investigation, as the source has not been found. Currently, the main transmission takes place from human to human.

Can the virus mutate?

Most viruses change over time, especially for viruses that have recently passed from animals to humans. The key question is whether this makes the virus more dangerous to people. This is a critical component of virus monitoring and prevention efforts.

Can you get the virus more than once?

Experts say there are different ways discharged patients can get sick from the virus.
Convalescent patients may not build up enough antibodies to develop immunity to SARS-CoV-2 and may be re-infected. The virus could also be "biphasic," which means that it lies dormant before causing new symptoms.
But some of the first cases of re-infections in China have been attributed to testing discrepancies.
On 21 February 2020, a discharged patient in the southwestern Chinese city of Chengdu was re-admitted 10 days after his discharge when a follow-up test was positive.

Quarantaine and isolation

What is quarantaine?

Quarantine is a precautionary measure to prevent the spread of an infectious disease. A person going into quarantine is not sick but has had contact with a patient with an infection. People who go into quarantine are not contagious. Someone goes into quarantine until the incubation period is over. This is the maximum time between the moment of possible infection and the moment when people develop symptoms of the disease. If people do not get sick during that period, the quarantine is lifted.

Quarantine at home?

We speak of home quarantine when someone who is not sick has to stay at home until it is certain that this person is not contagious to others. This period is typically less than 2 weeks in the case of the new coronavirus. The person in quarantine stays at home in a private room. Along with his or her housemates, they receive information from the government on measures to be taken to prevent possible spread.

Isolation?

A person who is kept in isolation is sick or there is a high possibility that they are sick. Isolation prevents these patients from infecting others. People can stay at home in isolation or be treated in a hospital depending on the severity of the symptoms and the infectiousness of the disease.

How do I prepare for quarantine or lockdown?

- Buy masks, hand cleanser, bleach, and gloves for at least a month, plus have all vital medications.
- Have a supply of painkillers and decongestants. Avoid drugs that suppress the immune system, such as prednisone.
- Smoking and drinking aggravate the risk of pneumonia; try to limit as much as possible.

Food shortages have not been a major problem in China, but it is a good idea to have non-perishable food for a month. Canned soups are especially recommended for their variety and ease of preparation.

Water is probably not critical, but if you live somewhere without drinkable tap water have a month's supply of bottled water. Fresh fruits and vegetables are often hard to get, so buy vitamin tablets, especially a supply of vitamin C.

Also remember other household necessities, especially things like toothpaste and shampoo, that may be forgotten when focused on food and water. In Hong Kong and Italy, supplies of toilet paper have dwindled. If you have pets at home, remember food and fresh litter for them.

Several people in quarantine mention missing delicacies and suggested stocking up on chocolate and sweets.

How to survive if the virus escalates?!

In a pandemic, you might also want to consider a hazmat suit. It might seem exaggerated now, but in unknown situations preparing for the worst is prudent. A hazmat suit can be re-used if you follow the correct procedures when putting it on and taking off.

A less extreme precaution is having a gas mask at hand. Several standards have been established by regulators for products such as gas masks and respirators — N95s filter 95% and P100s filter 99.97% of particles in the air.
It may seem strange to wear a gas mask, but in a truly deadly pandemic, it could become the norm. It certainly would be worthwhile to store gas masks as part of emergency preparation kits.

Gas masks can protect against a variety of harmful and toxic things that could be inhaled, including all known Chemical, Biological, Radiological, and Nuclear (CBRN) substances. This means that these gas masks and filters are not only suitable for pandemics, but they can also be life-saving in disaster scenarios.

The best strategies for surviving a pandemic

The best forms of protection against a pandemic are community strategies that minimize or mitigate threats. These strategies (often referred to as nonpharmaceutical interventions) can help reduce threats until a vaccine is available. When planning a survival strategy for a pandemic, it is important to think about the challenges you may face.

- Prepare backup plans in case regular public meetings are canceled.

- Plan for the possibility that regular services — such as those provided by hospitals and other healthcare institutions, banks, shops, restaurants, government offices and post offices — will be disrupted.

- Consider how to care for people with special needs in case the services they need are no longer available.

Avoid the unexpected

The lockdown has been particularly devastating in China for the tens of millions of people who were on family visits during the Lunar New Year Holiday and were stranded for weeks away from their own homes. Some migrant workers were forced into homelessness. Other people were forced to rely on the generosity of friends or strangers.

Foreign nationals have often had to apply for a special permit to extend a visa.

Minimize travel, especially internationally, if the spread of the virus continues. Take extra luggage and emergency money with you to prepare for the possibility of being stuck abroad for weeks longer than expected.

Financial measures

Small and medium enterprises in China are on the brink of collapse and salaries could be compromised.
Start thinking now about what a month of no or reduced income would mean for you. Try to minimize expenditures in the short-term to prepare for periods without pay. Prepare to move as much of your work life online as possible.

What is next?

The corona crisis is followed by the inevitable economic crisis. It will also cause a lot of misery. However, as always, the recession also offers opportunities. Recovery must come from innovation.

Unfortunately, we have to face the fact that a strong second wave of the pandemic is putting the recovery on hold and - more to the point - is likely to set the economy back a few steps. The collective inability to stop the circulation of the virus is forcing many countries, including the larger ones, to take further control and containment measures, with economic consequences. It is difficult to assess the precise impact of these measures. However, some conclusions can already be drawn in terms of economic forecasts.

The forced cessation of many activities and the mobilization of health care to fight the pandemic will have a major impact on economic activity.

Apart from the direct consequences, the new wave of the pandemic questions many certainties.

Households and businesses face more uncertainty about the future, which will further affect their consumption and investment behavior until the arrival and spread of a vaccine, expected by the summer of 2021. Until then, recovery is likely to be terribly slow, mainly because the authorities will be very cautious about reducing lockdown measures.

Disruption of the work process

- Ask your employer how business can/will continue during a pandemic.

- Ask your employer if you can work from home.

- Ask your employer or union about the leave policy during a pandemic.

- Plan for a possible reduction or temporary loss of income if you are unable to work, or if the company you work for is closed.

Stock your pantry

Have a supply of water and food that doesn't
spoil easily. Do not forget that public water
services may be interrupted.
Make sure you store food that:

- Is not perishable (has a long shelf life) and does
  not need to be refrigerated.

- You do not need to cook.

- Needs little or no water so you can save water

  for drinking.

Storing food stocks can also be useful in other
types of emergencies, such as power outages and
natural disasters. Make a checklist of items you
have at hand for a long stay at home.
Here's a simple list for 3 months of food for one
adult, equal to one month for one month:

- 75 pounds of grains—rice, oats, and
  others

- 25 pounds of canned meats
- 5 pounds of canned dairy—margarine, powdered eggs, and others
- 2 pounds of dried beans, peas, lentils, and others
- 6 pounds of dried fruit juice and concentrates
- 6 pounds of canned fruits
- 3 pounds of dried milk
- 25 pounds of peanut butter or substitute protein/fat source
- 3 of pounds of dried potatoes
- Salt
- 2 pounds of shortening oils
- 12 pounds of sugar or honey
- 9 pounds of canned or dried vegetables
- Enough vitamins and mineral supplements

Stay informed

Knowing the facts is the best preparation for a possible pandemic. Identify reliable sources for reliable information.
Check websites of your local and national government for information.
Listen to local and national radio, watch the news, and available web-based information.

For actual cases, deaths & recovered numbers, check:
https://www.worldometers.info/coronavirus

CPSIA information can be obtained
at www.ICGtesting.com
Printed in the USA
LVHW051026250121
677406LV00006B/630

9 789492 916150